Maurice Pledger

Billy Bunny
sticker book

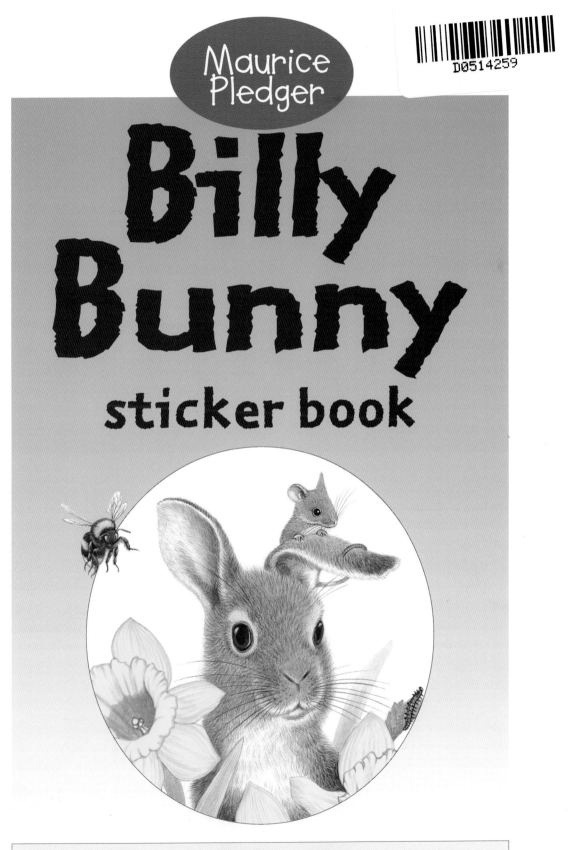

Counting and Colours

templar publishing

A TEMPLAR BOOK

First published in the UK in 2000 by Templar Publishing,
an imprint of The Templar Company Limited,
The Granary, North Street, Dorking, Surrey, RH4 1DN, UK
www.templarco.co.uk

This edition published in 2011

1 3 5 7 9 10 8

ISBN 978-1-8

Written by A.

Printed in Malaysia

How to use this book

On the following pages you'll find lots of sticker activities that will help you learn more about counting and colours as you go exploring with Billy Bunny and his animal friends.

You will find stickers of creatures in all sorts of colours. You can use them to complete the pictures as you follow Billy on his adventure to find a rainbow. Along the way, you can help him to count from 1 to 10 as well with his favourite fluffy friend, Charlie Chick.

Just turn to the back of the book and you'll find all the stickers you need to have lots of fun!

This is Billy Bunny, the baby rabbit. He lives in an enchanted forest far away with all his animal friends. Today, Billy Bunny is on a special adventure. He wants to see how many different colours he can find. If he's really lucky he might even find his very own rainbow. He's sure to get lots of help from all his furry forest friends. Why don't you join him and see what colourful discoveries you can make? Along the way you'll meet all sorts of different creatures that share Billy's forest home. And don't forget to use your stickers every time you meet a new animal friend!

Billy Bunny's rainbow

There are lots of colourful things to find in Billy's forest – dancing butterflies, beautiful birds and lots of pretty flowers. As you follow Billy on his adventure, see if you can help him collect objects in all the colours of the rainbow. Use your stickers to fill in the pictures of them opposite, then look out for them on the following pages.

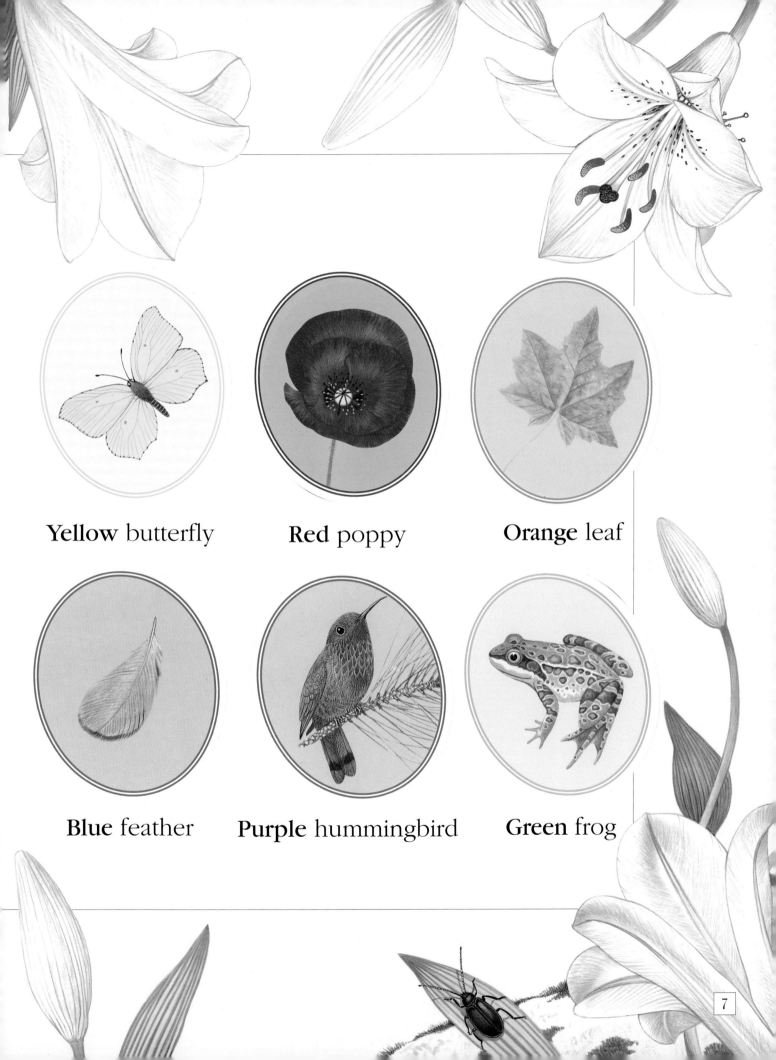

Yellow butterfly   **Red** poppy   **Orange** leaf

Blue feather   **Purple** hummingbird   **Green** frog

B illy has only just started on his adventure when he meets his good friend, Charlie Chick.
"Will you come with me to look for all the colours of the rainbow?" asks Billy, and Charlie agrees.

"Look! Here is a big **yellow** butterfly," chirps Charlie. Yellow is Charlie's favourite colour. Can you guess why? Now fill in the picture with some other yellow things that Billy and Charlie might find.

green   brown

Charlie's counting quest

Charlie Chick is learning to count all the way from 1 to 10. Can you help him by counting the creatures in the different groups opposite? Use your stickers to fill in the numbers as you go.

1

2

3

4

5

6

7

8

9

10

Charlie counts to 1

"Why don't you count all the colours that we find on our adventure?" suggests Billy Bunny. "So far we have found one colour – the colour yellow."

1

Help Billy and Charlie to keep a record of all the colours they find by adding a sticker of the yellow butterfly to the number panel below. Then add Charlie to the big picture, along with one ladybird, one mouse, one moth, one dragonfly and one bee for him to count.

B illy and Charlie reach the meadow where their friend Morris Mouse lives. He shows them a lovely **red** flower. It is called a poppy. What other red things do you think they might find on their adventure? Use your stickers to fill in the shapes with five red things.

Charlie counts to 2

"Now we have found two colours," says Charlie, "red and yellow. And, look, here are two flowers and two butterflies for me to count as well!" Use your stickers to fill in the pictures to give Charlie two chipmunks, two frogs, two wrens and two mice to count. And don't forget to add a red poppy to the number panel below.

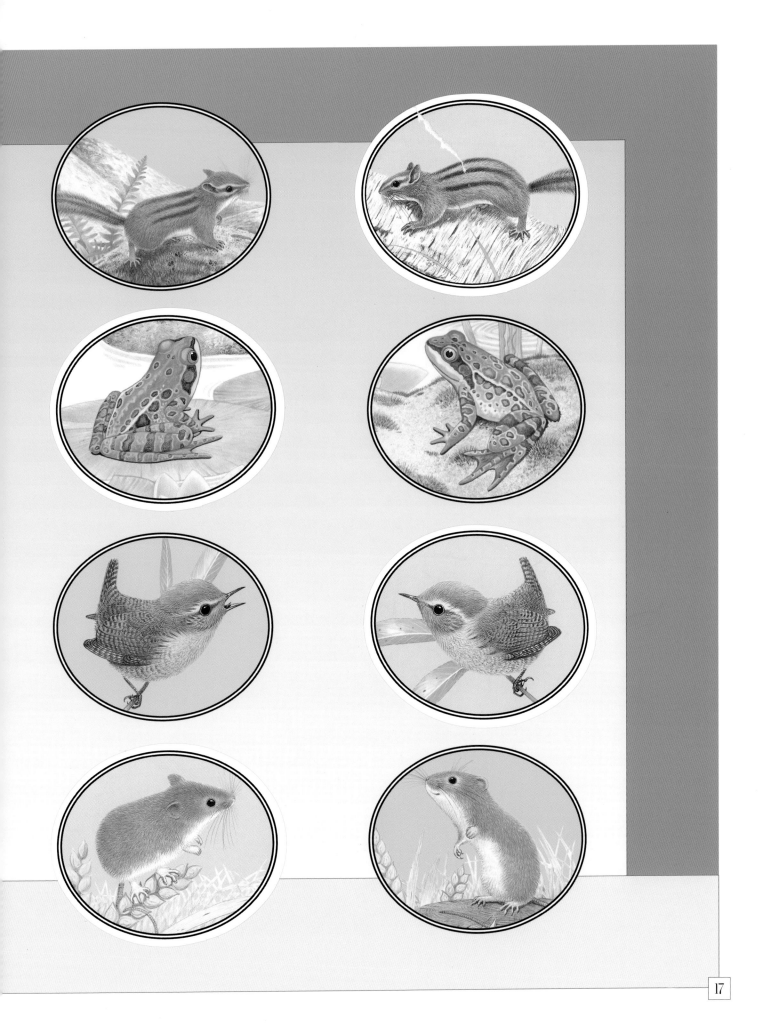

Next, Billy and Charlie meet Wally Wolf and his friend Freddy Fox. Freddy is covered in lovely **orange** fur and he gives Billy a beautiful orange leaf to add to his colour collection.

Can you think of some other orange things that Billy and Charlie might find on their walk through the wood? Use your stickers to add them to this picture.

Charlie counts to 3

"Now we have found three colours," says Charlie.
"And I can see three bumble bees," says Billy.
Use your stickers to add three beetles and three
butterflies to the picture. And don't forget
to add a sticker of an orange leaf to the
number panel below.

1   2   3

Make your own colourful picture of the meadow where Morris Mouse lives by adding stickers of red, yellow and orange things to this scene.

L ots of Billy's other forest friends have joined in his hunt for different colours. Here are Ozzy Owl, Sammy Skunk and Wally Wolf. Can you see what they have found? Why, it's a lovely **blue** feather for Billy's collection.

Use your stickers to
add some other blue
things to the picture.

Charlie counts to 4

Charlie is counting up to four. Add stickers to complete the groups so that Charlie can count four moths, four flowers, four bumble bees and four snails.

1   2   3   4

And, now that Billy and Charlie have found four colours, don't forget to add your sticker of a blue feather to the number panel below.

J enny Wren has told Billy where he can find a beautiful **purple** hummingbird. Use your sticker to put the bird in the picture.

Charlie counts to 5

There are lots of hummingbirds flying about in the forest. Can you see how many Charlie Chick has found feeding from the forest flowers? Use your stickers to add two missing birds to the picture to make five for Charlie to count. And don't forget to add the missing sticker to the number panel below.

1   2   3   4   5

L ook! Billy Bunny has found five insects and five flowers. Use your stickers to fill in the outline shapes so that there is an insect and a flower in all of the colours that Billy has found so far – yellow, red, orange, blue and purple.

own by the pond, Molly Mouse shows Billy a **green** frog. His name is Hoppy and he tells Billy about all sorts of other green things that he might see on the river bank.

Can you think what they might be?
Now use your stickers to add five
green creatures to the scene.

Charlie counts to 6

1 2 3 4 5

Charlie is counting frogs down by the pond. "Look, Billy!" he chirps. "I can count six frog friends!" Use your stickers to add the extra frog to the big picture to make six altogether. Don't forget to add the missing frog to the number panel below.

6

Lots of Billy's friends have gathered in the wood to help him look for different colours. Use your stickers to make a colourful picture of the things they find.

Other colours

Billy Bunny is very pleased with all the colours that he has found so far on his adventure – yellow, red, orange, blue, purple and green. "But there are lots of other colours for you to find, too!" says his friend Bobby Bear.

And when Billy looks he soon realises that Bobby is right – lots of his forest friends are other colours. Use your stickers to fill in the Portrait Gallery with some pictures of Billy's furry friends.

Oscar Otter is **brown**

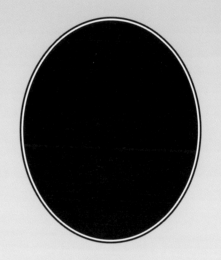

Bobby Bear is **black**

Polly Polar Bear is **white**

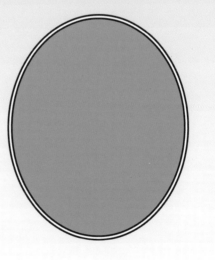

Ricky Raccoon is **grey**

Billy Bunny knows lots of animals that are **brown**. Here are his three friends Oscar Otter, Becky Beaver and Vinnie Vole. They all have lovely brown fur.

Now use your stickers to fill in the outline shapes
with five other things that are brown.

Charlie counts to 7

Now Charlie Chick has counted seven colours! He's also found seven of Billy's friends.

Molly Mouse

1 2 3 4 5

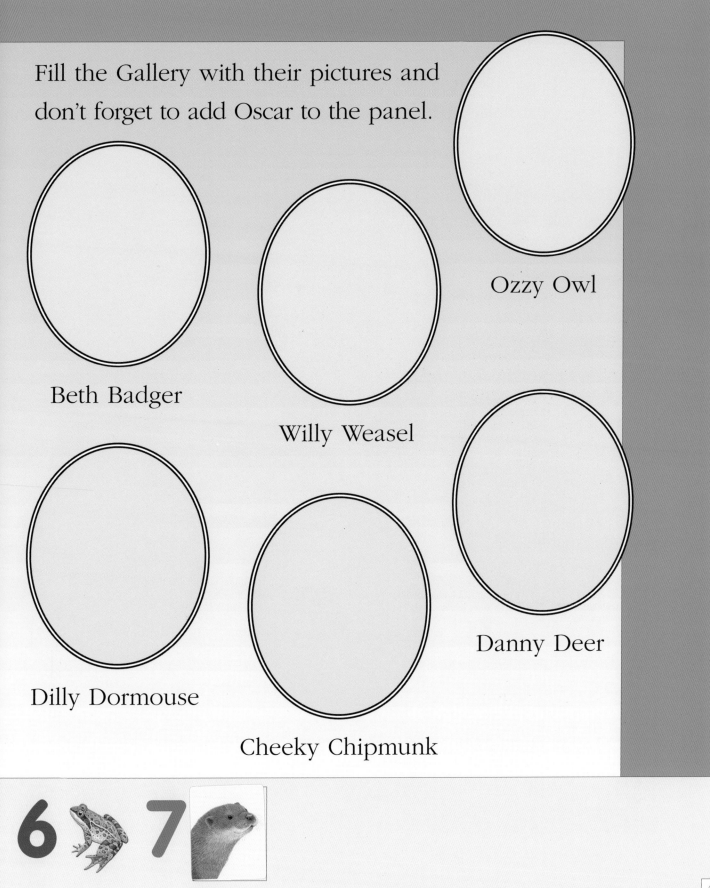

Fill the Gallery with their pictures and don't forget to add Oscar to the panel.

Ozzy Owl

Beth Badger

Willy Weasel

Danny Deer

Dilly Dormouse

Cheeky Chipmunk

6 7

Bobby Bear is covered in lovely **black** fur. But there are lots of other black things to find in the forest as well.

Use your stickers to fill in the outline shapes with five black things that Billy might find on his adventure.

Charlie counts to 8

Charlie Chick is excited. Billy Bunny has found a butterfly and a ladybird down by the old log. Can you use your stickers to add six more creepy crawlies to the picture? And don't forget to add a sticker of Bobby, the black bear cub, to the number panel below.

1   2   3   4   5

6 7 8

H ere is Polly Polar Bear. She is Bobby Bear's cousin and she is covered from head to toe in soft **white** fur. She lives far away from the forest where Bobby and Billy live, in a place where the land is often covered with snow. Lots of her animal friends are white too. Use your stickers to put pictures of them in the Portrait Gallery.

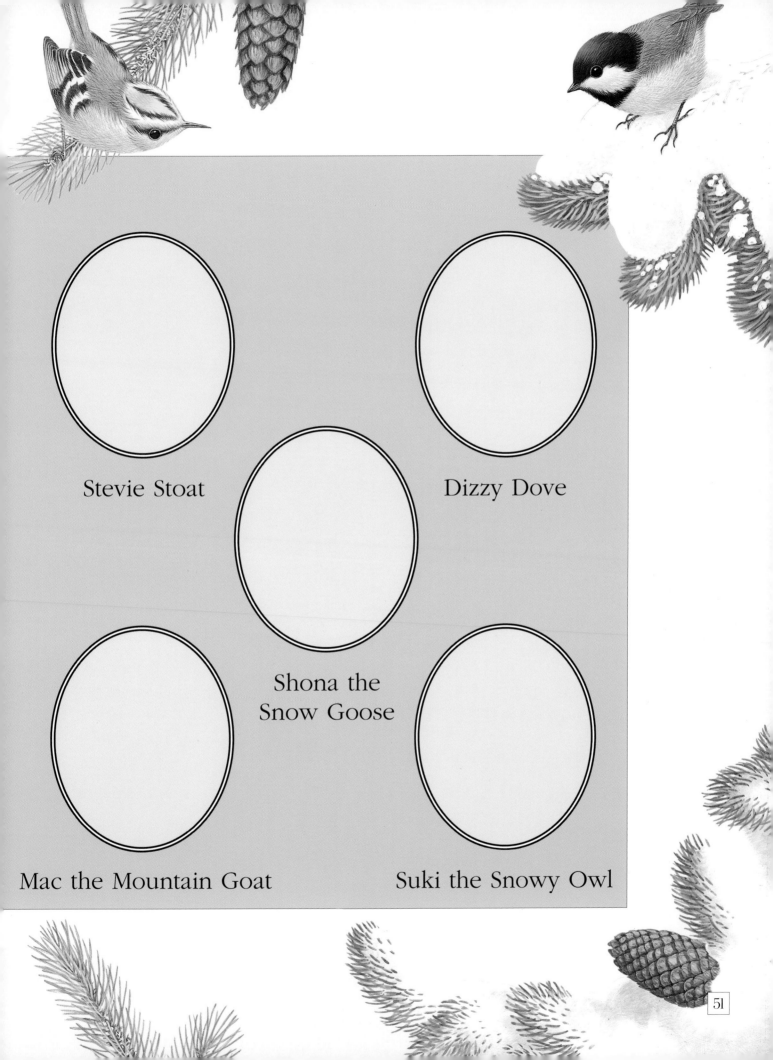

Stevie Stoat

Dizzy Dove

Shona the
Snow Goose

Mac the Mountain Goat

Suki the Snowy Owl

51

Charlie counts to 9

 Charlie is counting all the animals that he can see in this picture of Polly Polar Bear's snowy home. He can see four animals already.

1 2 3 4 5

Use your stickers to add five more so that there are nine animals for Charlie to count and don't forget to add your sticker to the number panel below.

6 7 8 9

Billy Bunny has met his old friend Ricky Raccoon. Billy tells him all about his adventure and the colours he has found. "And what about you?" asks Ricky. "You and I are the same colour – the colour **grey**!" Use your stickers to fill the Portrait Gallery with some other grey animals.

Percy Pigeon

Wally Wolf

Sidney Seal

Sammy Squirrel

Charlie counts to 10

Look what Billy and Charlie have found in the forest glade – a crowd of fluttering butterflies. Add five more butterflies to the picture so that there are ten butterflies for them to count.

1   2   3   4   5

6 **7** **8** **9** **10**

Can you count to ten like Charlie? Add ten stickers to this riverside scene. Then count all the different creatures in the picture.

Billy's colours

Billy Bunny has discovered so many colours on his adventure that he is having trouble remembering all their names!

Can you help him by putting the right colour sticker next to all the colourful things he has found?

Charlie counts from 1 to 10

Help Charlie Chick practise his counting one more time. Use your stickers to fill in the missing objects next to each number. Then count them again with him, all the way from 1 to 10.
Well done, Charlie Chick!

1

2

3

4

5

6

7

8

9

10

B illy and Charlie are tired after their long walk. "Let's go and sit down by the river," suggests Charlie. And who should they meet on the river bank but Katie Kingfisher. Katie has lovely feathers of blue and orange. Can you think of some other animals that are more than one colour?

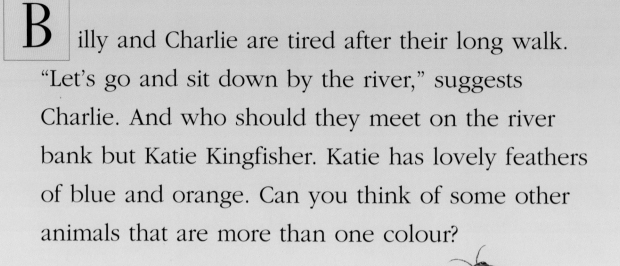

Use your stickers to fill in the outline shapes with some multi-coloured creatures.

Billy has found lots of multi-coloured creatures in this forest clearing. Use your stickers to add them to the picture. Can you say all the colours that they are?

What colour am I?

Now that you have met all sorts of colourful creatures, see if you can use your stickers to fill in this simple quiz.

Who is grey and has found a blue feather for Billy?

Who is black with yellow stripes?

 Who is red with black spots?

Who is covered in lovely orange fur?

Who is covered in fluffy yellow feathers?

Who is green and hops across the lily pads?

Who is purple and drinks nectar from the forest flowers?

Who is blue and orange and lives by the river?

Hurray! Billy and Charlie have found a rainbow at last. Now use your stickers to make your own picture of Billy and his rainbow.

How to use your stickers

Look for the page numbers on the sticker sheets. They will help you to find the right stickers for the different activities in this book.

Peel each sticker carefully from its backing sheet and stick it in the right place in the book. You can use the stickers again and again if you remember to treat them carefully.

Sheets 6 and 12 contain lots and lots of stickers for you to make up your own pictures. You can use them with the big scenes in the book. Or you could draw your own picture of the special place where Billy Bunny lives with all his animal friends and stick them on that!

Beetles for pages 20/21

Butterflies for pages 20/21

ers for pages 18/19

Stick

Stickers for pages 22/23 can be found on Sticker Sheet 6

Stickers for pages 24/25

Stickers for pages 26/27

Sticker Sheet

4

Stickers for pages 32/33

Hummingbird for page 29

Hummingbirds for pages 30/31

Stickers for pages 34/35

Sticker Sheet

5

Stickers for pages 38/39 can be found on Sticker Sheet 6

Frog for pages 36/37

Stickers for pages 40/41

Stickers for pages 42/43

Stickers for pages 22/23 – The Meadow

Stickers for pages 38/39 – The Wood

Stickers for pages 46/47

Stickers for pages 52/53

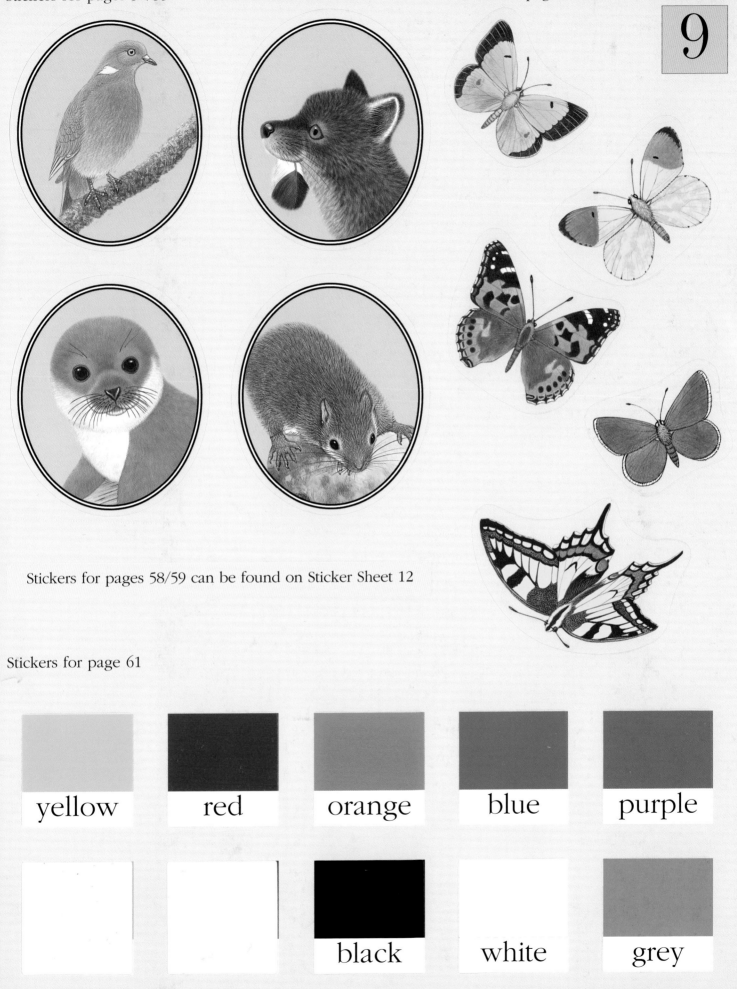

Stickers for pages 54/55

Stickers for pages 56/57

Sticker Sheet

9

Stickers for pages 58/59 can be found on Sticker Sheet 12

Stickers for page 61

yellow   red   orange   blue   purple

black   white   grey

Stickers for pages 68/69

Stickers for pages 70/71 can be found on Sticker Sheet 12

Stickers for pages 58/59 – The Riverside

Stickers for page 70/71 – Billy's Rainbow